posers

80 delightful hurdles for reasonably agile minds

illustrations by jo ann stover

POSERS

by
philip kaplan

harper & row, publishers
new york and evanston

Library of Congress Catalog Card Number: 63–8129

to Esther

introduction

Three thousand years ago, King Solomon displayed the wisdom for which he was widely acclaimed by solving a poser involving two of his ministers.

These men jointly owned a piece of land, but, for reasons which history does not clarify, decided to end their partnership.

Such a minor affair certainly would never have come to the king's attention except that the execution of the project led to all sorts of complications. The principal difficulty lay in the fact that the land was shaped like an octopus with fingers of land jutting out of the main body at various places. The best surveyors in the country were called in to perform the necessary surgery in dividing the land in half, but, learned as they were, their talents were not equal to the task.

Solomon heard of their difficulty through the palace grapevine and ordered the ministers to appear before him. He listened to their story and then, substituting common sense for the surveyors' instruments, solved the poser very simply. "Measure the land as best thou canst," he said to the first man, "and mark off clearly the boundaries of the two halves. If thou makest one half larger than the other, thou doest so at thine own risk for thy neighbor shall have his choice of halves and thou the remainder."

'In the pages which follow, you will find a refreshing variety of posers. Fortunately, it doesn't take a Solomon to solve them —all it takes is a reasonably agile mind and the desire to use it. To put it another way, no mathematics (except the very simplest arithmetic) or any other special knowledge is required—just plain common sense.

The posers are divided into eight sets of ten each, and within each set (except the last one, which is special) they are arranged roughly according to difficulty. The first and second of each set might conceivably be solved by a bright eight-year-old; the third and possibly the fourth by a bright twelve-year-old or not so bright adult. After that, it's every man for himself.

If you feel like measuring your poser-solving ability, each set can be treated as a test. You score 10 points for each poser solved within the liberal time period allotted or 7 points if it takes you up to twice the allotted time. And, if you are the persistent type, you score 3 points no matter when divine inspiration descends. There are score cards at the end of each group and detailed solutions appear at the end of the book.

If taking a test is not to your taste, ignore the above paragraph and take your posers straight. They will give you just as much satisfaction that way. After you've gotten the answers (or peeked in the back), I highly recommend a social evening with friends at which you can act as interlocutor, judge and jury. The competition will be keen; some of the "solutions" will be weird and the evening will pass more quickly than you can imagine.

I am reluctant to give any advice about recommended methods for attacking posers because my wife violates almost every rule of sound analysis but usually comes up with the right answers. She seems to operate on an intuitive level where rules of correct procedure would be a nuisance at least and possibly downright harmful. I will confine myself, therefore, to just one general remark which I promise won't cramp anyone's style. Here it is—*do* read the posers carefully to establish clearly what the facts are but *do not* assume anything unless it is specifically stated. Without knowing all the facts, you haven't the necessary instruments for operating successfully and making unwarranted assumptions may yield solutions but not to the poser at hand. End of advice.

The last ten posers are especially delightful but very tough. This group is intended for abnormal people who aren't happy unless their mental resources are taxed to the breaking point. Normal people will also find them interesting even though the solution section of the book will have to be consulted for most of the answers.

poser group one

score 10, 7, 3 or 0
score card on page 8

1.

A man who wears either blue or brown socks keeps them all in the same drawer in a state of complete disorder. In total there are 20 blue and 20 brown socks in the drawer.

Assuming that there is insufficient light for the man to see the color of the socks, how many must he take out of the drawer to be sure that he has a matching pair?

2 minutes

2.

A chemist had been working on discovering a liquid in which all substances will dissolve. One day he announced that he had a bottle full of the desired liquid.

What's wrong with his claim?

3 minutes

3.

Two cars start out together and continue to move in the same direction. One of them never exceeds the speed limit, which is 40 miles per hour. The second car never gets ahead of the first car, yet the driver of the second car legitimately gets a ticket for speeding.

How can this happen?

7 minutes

4.

A game is played in which two players participate. A group of markers (coins, marbles, matchsticks, etc.) is reduced in turn by each player by removing from the group at least 1 but not more than 4 markers. The player who takes the last marker is the winner.

Assuming a group of 17 markers, what move would you make if it was your turn and how would you continue to play to win?

15 minutes

5.

A train one mile long travels at the rate of one mile a minute through a tunnel which is one mile long.

How long will it take for the train to pass completely through the tunnel?

7 minutes

6.

How many brothers and sisters are there in a family in which each boy has as many sisters as brothers but each of the girls has twice as many brothers as sisters?

5 minutes

7.

All the outside surfaces of a 3″ x 3″ x 3″ cube (including the top and bottom) are painted red. Then the cube is cut into 27 cubes, 1″ x 1″ x 1″.

How many 1″ cubes do not have any painted surfaces?

10 minutes

8.

Which is worth more, a carton full of $5 gold pieces or an identical carton half full of $10 gold pieces?

7 minutes

9.

A man had no money but he had a gold chain which contained 23 links. His landlord agreed to accept 1 link per day in payment for rent. The man, however, wanted to keep the chain as intact as possible because he expected to receive a sum of money with which he would buy back what he had given the landlord. Of course, opened links can be used in payment too and "change" can be made with links already given to the landlord.

What is the smallest number of links which must be opened in order for the man to be able to pay his rent each day for 23 days?

45 minutes

10.

A game is played by 3 players in which the one who loses must double the amount of money that each of the other 2 players has at that time.

Each of the 3 players loses 1 game and at the conclusion of the 3 games each man has $16.

How much money did each man start with?

20 minutes

poser group one score

1 ——	6 ——
2 ——	7 ——
3 ——	8 ——
4 ——	9 ——
5 ——	10 ——

total score ——

Poser I. Q.
About 50 is average
65-75 is exceptional
Over 75 is outstanding

poser group two

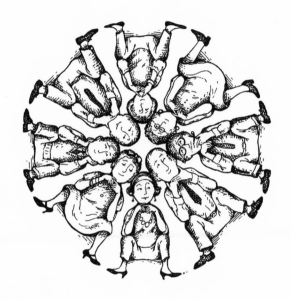

score 10, 7, 3 or 0
score card on page 16

11.

A man has $1.15 made up of 6 American coins. With these coins, however, he cannot make change of a dollar, nor of a half dollar, quarter, dime or nickel.
Which 6 coins does he have?

4 minutes

12.

A signalman has 3 lights, 1 red, 1 white and 1 blue. Signals can be made by displaying any 2 of the 3 lights together. (The position of the lights is not significant.)
How many different signals can be made in accordance with the above?

2 minutes

13.

Sixteen bowling balls are placed inside of a square wooden rack in 4 rows of 4 so that they are held firmly together.

How many additional balls are required to complete a pyramid on top of the 16-ball foundation?

6 minutes

14.

If 50 men enter a singles tennis tournament, how many matches are required to determine the winner? Of course, a player is eliminated as soon as he loses a match.

10 minutes

15.

In a certain town, there are two groups of men—one group always tells the truth; the other group always lies.

A stranger arrived in this town and asked one of the natives whether he was a Truth Teller or a Liar. The native answered but the stranger didn't hear the answer. Two other natives, A and B, who overheard the conversation were questioned by the stranger as to what the first man had said. A replied, "He said he was a Truth Teller." Native B replied, "He said he was a Liar."

Can you tell which of the two men, A or B, is a Truth Teller and which is a Liar?

7 minutes

16.

An automobile has traveled 20,000 miles.

If 5 tires were used equally in accumulating this mileage, how many miles' wear did each tire sustain?

15 minutes

17.

A man has two girl friends, one living uptown and the other downtown. Since he has no special preference for either friend, he takes whichever train gets to the station first. He arrives at random times but finds that he is visiting his uptown friend much more often than the other despite the fact that both the uptown and downtown trains are on schedules which bring them to his station equally often. Since the same thing has been happening for a very long time, chance has been ruled out as the reason.

Can you explain the frequency of his uptown trips?

15 minutes

18.

The law for the sale of alcoholic beverages in some states provides that beer cannot be sold after a certain hour, but permits a customer to consume, after the curfew, what has been served before the deadline.

As the curfew approached, each of 2 men ordered sufficient beer to anticipate his probable requirements. The first man ordered and paid for 5 cans and the second man ordered and paid for 3 cans.

As the curfew sounded, a mutual friend approached and, being thirsty too, suggested that he be permitted to share in the refreshments which had so providentially been provided. Permission having been granted, the 3 men shared equally in dispatching the beer.

The third man thanked his friends and then put down 80¢ in payment for the beer he had consumed, which was to be divided equitably between the other 2 men.

Should 50¢ be given to the man who had bought 5 cans and 30¢ to the other, or is some other division of the spoils indicated? If so, how should the money be divided?

20 minutes

19.

Place 10 coins in such a way that they lie in 5 straight lines and on each line there are 4 coins. (There is more than one solution.)

20 minutes

20.

Nine dots are arranged in a square formation in 3 rows of 3.

Draw 4 straight lines, the second beginning where the first ends, the third beginning where the second ends, and the fourth beginning where the third ends so that each dot is on at least one line.

20 minutes

```
. . .
. . .
. . .
```

poser group two score

11 ———		16 ———
12 ———		17 ———
13 ———		18 ———
14 ———		19 ———
15 ———		20 ———

total score ———

Poser I. Q.
About 50 is average
*   65-75 is exceptional*
Over 75 is outstanding

poser group three

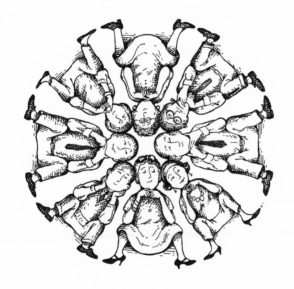

score 10, 7, 3 or 0
score card on page 24

21.

Three couples must get across a river using a boat which cannot hold more than 2 people. None of the men will allow his wife to be on the same side of the river or in the boat with any other man (or men) unless he also is present.

Assuming that both the husbands and wives can row, how do the 3 couples get across under the stated conditions?

15 minutes

22.

There are 6 matches in a horizontal row, 3 with heads up followed by 3 with heads down. The position of the matches can be changed by turning over any 2 adjacent matches.

In 3 moves, show how to change the position of the matches so that the head of the first match is up, the second down, the third up, fourth down, etc.

5 minutes

23.

A container holds exactly 8 quarts of liquid and is filled to the top. Two empty containers are also available, one of which can hold 5 quarts and the other 3 quarts.

Without the use of any other measuring devices, the liquid can be divided into equal parts of 4 quarts each simply by pouring from one container to another.

How is this done?

15 minutes

24.

If a standard-sized cigarette can be "rolled" out of 6 standard-sized cigarette butts, how many cigarettes can be made and smoked from 36 butts?

HINT: *The answer is not 6.*

7 minutes

25.

A game is played by two players. Markers are arranged in piles and each person moves by taking as many markers from any one pile as he wishes. The player who is able to take the last marker is the winner.

If the play has progressed to the point where there is a pile of 5 markers, a pile of 3 markers and a pile of 1 marker left, what move should you now make to assure that you will win no matter how your opponent moves?

20 minutes

26.

A lady at a card party announced that she could perform a "magic" card trick. She asked her friend to turn over 20 cards and insert them at random, face up, into the rest of the deck. Next the cards were to be thoroughly shuffled and then the 20 cards at the top of the deck were to be handed back to her under the table.

Presumably, there are more turned-over cards in the remainder of the deck than in the top 20 cards, so the lady states that without looking at the cards (by feel alone) she will turn over additional cards so that the total number turned over will be identical with the number turned over in the remainder of the deck. How does she perform this remarkable trick without magic?

20 minutes

27.

Three men had hidden a hoard of gold coins (less than 100) before they retired. During the night, one man awoke, counted the coins and found that he could divide the loot into 3 equal parts if he first took 1 coin for himself. He then took 1 coin and ⅓ of the rest and went back to bed. Shortly thereafter, the second man repeated the procedure, again taking 1 coin for himself before taking ⅓ of the remainder. Needless to say, the third man awoke and did the same.

In the morning it was found that the remaining coins again totaled 1 more than could be equally divided into 3 parts.

How many coins were originally hidden?

25 minutes

28.

A certain battalion had between 2,000 and 3,000 men. It was desired to divide the battalion into not more than 9 groups each containing the same number of men. However, it was discovered that this couldn't be done because there was always 1 man left over.

How many men were there in the battalion?

25 minutes

29.

Twenty artisans work for a king making gold objects each of which is supposed to weigh exactly 1 ounce. The work of each man can easily be identified because each artisan is assigned to work on a different object. It has come to the king's attention that one of the men is making his objects using ⅛ ounce of gold less than he should, and stealing the difference.

How can the king, in one weighing, determine which of the 20 artisans is the culprit?

25 minutes

30.

There are 3 men—Arthur, Ben and Charles—each of whom has 2 occupations from among the following— doctor, engineer, teacher, painter, writer and lawyer. No 2 men have the same occupation.

1. The doctor had lunch with the teacher.
2. The teacher and writer went fishing with Arthur.
3. The painter is related to the engineer.
4. The doctor hired the painter to do a job.
5. Ben lives next door to the writer.
6. Charles beat Ben and the painter at tennis.

Which 2 occupations is each man engaged in?

30 minutes

poser group three score

21 ———		26 ———
22 ———		27 ———
23 ———		28 ———
24 ———		29 ———
25 ———		30 ———

total score ———

Poser I. Q.
About 50 is average
* 65-75 is exceptional*
Over 75 is outstanding

poser group four

score 10, 7, 3 or 0
score card on page 32

31.

A man is served 2 mugs of coffee but only one saucer. He had intended to keep the coffee in both mugs warm as long as possible by putting the saucers on top of the cups.

Assuming that the man has no other equipment than that mentioned above, what can he do to keep both mugs warm even though he has only one saucer?

1 minute

32.

If a hat and coat cost $110 and the coat cost $100 more than the hat, how much does the coat cost?

6 minutes

33.

Twenty-five dots are arranged in a square formation in 5 rows of 5.

How can 12 of these dots be connected with straight lines to form a perfect cross which has 5 dots inside it and 8 dots outside?

20 minutes

34.

A bookworm eats his way from page 1 of Volume I to the last page of Volume II of a two-volume work. The books are standing on a bookshelf in the usual manner with the bindings facing out.

If the pages of each volume are 3″ thick and the covers ¼″, through how many inches did the bookworm chew?

HINT: *The answer is not 6½″.*

15 minutes

35.

If you could count the number of bacteria in a certain container, you would find that there were twice as many there as on the previous day. And if you counted again on the following day, you would find twice as many as you found today.

Assuming this rate of growth to be normal for bacteria, and that a certain container would be full of bacteria in 60 days, on which day would the container be half full?

7 minutes

36.

Five men and a boat are on one side of a stream and 5 women are on the opposite bank. The men want to get to the opposite shore and it seems that the women, too, want to cross the stream. Only 1 man and 1 woman know how to row. Also, it would be undesirable to have more men than women either in the boat or on either shore.

If the boat can hold no more than 3 people, how can the mission be accomplished in 7 crossings?

25 minutes

37.

If it takes 7 seconds for a clock to strike 7, how long does it take for the same clock to strike 10?

20 minutes

38.

Suppose you had a gallon of water and a gallon of alcohol. You take a glass of alcohol and pour it into the water and mix thoroughly. Then you take a glass of the mixture which you have just created and pour it back into the alcohol.

Does the alcohol now contain more or less water than the amount of alcohol remaining in the original water container, or the same amount?

15 minutes

39.

A man is about to leave his home to visit a friend. He glances at his clock and notices that it is not going. Before leaving, he winds his clock and notes the time shown on this clock. On arrival at his friend's house he immediately notes the correct time and, after completing his visit, he again notes the time on his friend's clock and then he goes home.

With the information he has obtained, the man goes directly to his clock, notes the time on it and then is able to set his clock to the correct time.

How was he able to do this, assuming that the walking time to and from his friend's house was the same?

20 minutes

40.

A passenger train takes 3 times as long to pass a freight train when they both are going in the same direction as when they are going in opposite directions.

Assuming that the trains travel at uniform speeds, how many times faster than the freight train is the passenger train going?

30 minutes

poser group four score

31 ———		36 ———
32 ———		37 ———
33 ———		38 ———
34 ———		39 ———
35 ———		40 ———

total score ———

Poser I. Q.
About 50 is average
  65-75 is exceptional
Over 75 is outstanding

poser group five

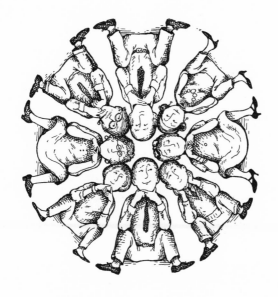

score 10, 7, 3 or 0
score card on page 40

41.

A man was asked how many rabbits and chickens he had in his yard. He replied, "Between the two there are 60 eyes and 86 feet."

Although the reply was not exactly responsive, can you determine how many chickens and rabbits the man had?

10 minutes

42.

A man buys a pair of shoes which sell for $6 and pays for them with a $10 bill. The storekeeper doesn't have the change, so he gets the $10 bill changed by a neighboring shopkeeper. Later, the shopkeeper discovers that the $10 bill was counterfeit. Naturally, the storekeeper who sold the shoes must give back $10 to his neighbor.

If the storekeeper originally paid $3 for the shoes, what did he lose on this transaction?

15 minutes

43.

There are 4 black, 4 red and 4 white marbles in a box.

How many marbles must one take out (without looking at them) to be sure that there are at least 2 of one color among the marbles selected?

5 minutes

44.

A window is in the shape of a square 4 feet across by 4 feet down. Half the area of the square window was painted, yet the clear part remains a square and still measures 4 feet from top to bottom and 4 feet from side to side.

How can this be done?

15 minutes

45.

An army group consisting of approximately 1,000 men is marching in a square formation. An attack from the enemy reduced the group by 10 men and they were re-formed into 6 equal squares. Again the group was attacked and this time there were 6 casualties. The group was again re-formed into 7 equal squares.

How many men were there in the original group?

25 minutes

46.

In a certain town, there were 3 classes of people. The first class always told the truth; the second class always lied; and the third class sometimes told the truth and sometimes lied. One day as 3 men, one from each class, sat talking, a stranger approached and asked the man at the left, "What kind of man sits next to you?" "A liar," answered the first man. "What kind of man are you?" asked the stranger of the middle man. "I sometimes tell the truth and sometimes I lie," he answered. "And what kind of man is the man next to you?" asked the stranger of the last man. "He always tells the truth," replied the third man.

From this scintillating conversation, can you tell the class to which each man belonged?

20 minutes

47.

A spindle has 4 discs of different sizes on it. The largest disc is on the bottom and the others are on top of it in decreasing size. Two empty spindles are also available.

It is required to remove all the discs and transfer them to one of the other spindles so that the largest is again on the bottom and the others are again in size place. One disc is to be moved at a time and in no case can a larger disc be on top of a smaller one.

How many moves are required to make this transfer?

20 minutes

48.

A man has 9 coins which are identical in appearance, but actually 1 of the coins is lighter than the other 8.

How can the man determine which coin is defective if he is allowed only 2 weighings on a balance scale?

25 minutes

49.

A man usually arrives at his station at 6 p.m. and his wife drives him home. One day he arrived at 5 p.m. and started walking home. He met his wife en route to the station, got into the car and drove home, arriving 10 minutes earlier than usual.

Assuming that his wife always meets him exactly at 6 p.m., how long did the man walk before being picked up by his wife?

20 minutes

50.

Three men have been blindfolded and told that a spot may or may not have been placed on each of their foreheads. If, when the blindfolds are removed, a man sees a spot on either or both of the foreheads of the other men, he is to raise his hand. Actually, a spot was placed on the forehead of each man so that when the blindfolds were removed, all three men raised their hands.

The men were also told that as soon as any of them could determine whether or not he had a spot on his own forehead, he was to announce this fact.

After five minutes had elapsed, one of the men announced that he had a spot on his forehead. How was he able to determine this?

30 minutes

poser group five score

41 ———		46 ———	
42 ———		47 ———	
43 ———		48 ———	
44 ———		49 ———	
45 ———		50 ———	

total score ———

Poser I. Q.
About 50 is average
65-75 is exceptional
Over 75 is outstanding

poser group six

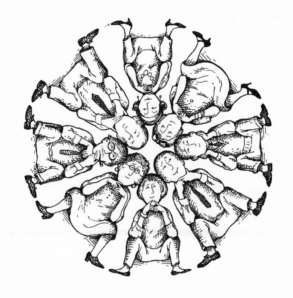

score 10, 7, 3 or 0
score card on page 48

51.

Three boats traveling east in a narrow stream meet 3 boats going west. The stream is not wide enough to allow the boats to pass each other. Fortunately, there is an inlet which can hold 1 boat.

Assuming, as is normal, that the boats can move both forward and back, how do the boats pass each other?

15 minutes

52.

A man bought something for $60 and sold it for $70. Then he bought it back for $80 and resold it for $90. How much profit, if any, did he make?

4 minutes

53.

Two men agreed to participate in an unusual horserace. It was agreed that the man whose horse crossed the finish line first would be the loser and the man whose horse crossed the finish line second would be declared the winner. Naturally, as the contestants approached the finish line, they made their horses go slower and slower until finally they came to a halt, got off their horses and sat down at the side of the road to discuss the situation. Just then a stranger came along who listened to their problem and suggested a course of action. The men immediately jumped on the horses and sped toward the finish line.

What did the stranger suggest, consistent with the original arrangements, which made the men spring into action?

15 minutes

54.

Two stations are 50 miles apart. Two trains start toward each other at the same time on a single track.

Just as the trains start out, a bird leaves the first train and flies directly to the other train, and as soon as the bird reaches the second train it starts back toward the first train. This goes on until the trains meet.

If both trains travel at 25 miles per hour and the bird flies at 100 miles per hour, how many miles will the bird have flown before the trains meet?

15 minutes

55.

In a domino set there is a domino which combines every number, including 0, with every other number.

In a set that runs from double-0 through double-6, how many dominoes are there?

20 minutes

56.

It was definitely established that 1 of 4 men committed a crime. Following are the statements made by each of the suspects.

      Abe: Bert did it.
      Bert: Dan did it.
      Charlie: I didn't do it.
      Dan: Bert lied when he said I did it.
If only one statement is true, who is the criminal?

20 minutes

57.

*Three containers hold 19, 13 and 7 quarts respectively.
The 13- and 7-quart containers are full but the 19-quart
container is empty.*

*How can you measure out 10 quarts by using just the
3 containers mentioned above?*

25 minutes

58.

*How can 6 cigarettes be placed (without bending or
breaking any of them) so that each of the 6 cigarettes
will touch each of the others?*

HINT: *The cigarettes do not all have to rest on one
surface.*

25 minutes

59.

Ten checkers are placed in a straight line. A checker can be moved in either direction but must jump over 2 adjacent checkers and land on top of the next one, making a "king." Jumping over a king is equivalent to jumping over 2 adjacent checkers.

Under these rules, how can you produce 5 kings out of the 10 checkers? (There is more than one solution.)

25 minutes

60.

A ship leaves New York for Liverpool every day and a ship leaves Liverpool for New York every day at the same time. The trip across takes exactly 6 days.

How many ships from Liverpool will a ship leaving New York today pass by the time it arrives in Liverpool, including any Liverpool ships met at the New York or Liverpool docks?

15 minutes

poser group six score

51 ———		56 ———	
52 ———		57 ———	
53 ———		58 ———	
54 ———		59 ———	
55 ———		60 ———	

total score ———

Poser I. Q.
About 50 is average
* 65-75 is exceptional*
* Over 75 is outstanding*

poser group seven

score 10, 7, 3 or 0
score card on page 56

61.

A brick balances evenly with ¾ of a pound and ¾ of a brick.

What is the weight of the whole brick?

6 minutes

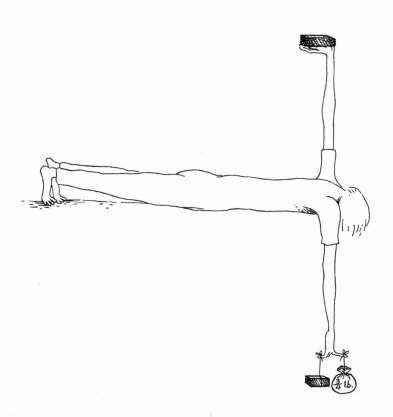

62.

Ten bowling pins are set up in the usual way forming a triangle with the point facing the bowler.

How can 3 pins be moved so that the 10 pins are still set up in the conventional manner but with the point of the triangle away from the bowler?

10 minutes

63.

A well is 10 feet deep. A frog climbs up 5 feet during the day but falls back 4 feet during the night.

Assuming that the frog starts at the bottom of the well, on which day does he get to the top?

10 minutes

64.

A pie is to be cut into pieces by using 5 straight line cuts of a knife.

If the pieces cannot be moved, and each piece can be of a different size, how many pieces can the pie be cut into?

20 minutes

65.

A woman lost her umbrella on a bus. She remembered that the number on the plate showing the bus number was a perfect square* and, also, if the plate was turned upside down, the number would still be a perfect square (not 1). The bus company has only 500 buses numbered from 1 to 500.

What was the number of the bus?

* *A perfect square, incidentally, is a number which can be divided into 2 identical factors. Examples are 9 which is 3 x 3; 16 which is 4 x 4; 25 which is 5 x 5, etc.*

15 minutes

66.

There are 3 boxes on a table. One contains 2 black marbles; another 2 white marbles; and the third 1 black and 1 white marble. Each box was suitably labeled but somehow the box labels were switched so that every box now has an incorrect label.

You are allowed to take 1 marble at a time out of any box without looking inside and by this process determine the correct contents of the 3 boxes.

What is the smallest number of samplings required to determine the contents of the boxes?

15 minutes

67.

A man has a balance scale on which he wants to be able to weigh objects weighing any whole number of pounds from 1 up to and including 13. In order to do this, he requires 3 weights which can be used on either or both sides of the scale.

What are the 3 required weights?

20 minutes

68.

One hundred applicants applied for a certain job. It was found that, of these 100, 10 applicants had had no mathematics training and no biology training; 70 had had some mathematics and 82 had had some biology.

How many applicants had had both mathematics and biology training?

20 minutes

69.

A man put his license plate, consisting of 5 *different* numbers, on his car upside down and discovered that the number still could be read. However, the value of the number had increased by 78,633.

What was his license number?

20 minutes

70.

A man has 5 sections of bracelet, each section consisting of 4 links.

If it costs 10 cents to cut open a link and 10 cents to solder it together again, what is the cheapest method and how much would it cost to join the 5 pieces into one closed bracelet?

25 minutes

poser group seven score

61 ———	64 ———	67 ———
62 ———	65 ———	68 ———
63 ———	66 ———	69 ———

70 ———   total score ———

Poser I. Q.   *65-75 is exceptional*
About 50 is average   *Over 75 is outstanding*

groups one to seven—average score

group 1 ———	(p. 8)	5 ———	(p. 40)
2 ———	(p. 16)	6 ———	(p. 48)
3 ———	(p. 24)	7 ———	(p. 56)
4 ———	(p. 32)	total ———	

AVERAGE SCORE (total divided by 7) _____

super poser group eight

score 10, 7, 3 or 0
score card on page 64

71.

A wooden cube, 3" on a side, is to be cut into 27 1" cubes by a buzz saw. This can be done by 6 cuts of the saw while keeping the pieces together.

Can the number of cuts be reduced by rearranging the pieces after each cut? If yes, how is it done; if no, prove that it can't be done.

25 minutes

72.

Two men play draw poker as follows: All cards are turned face upward. The first man chooses any 5 cards he wishes. Then the second man chooses any 5 of the remaining cards. The first man discards as many cards as he wishes (all 5 if he so chooses) and replaces his discards from the remaining cards. His discards are put aside. The second man then discards and replaces those cards. The person who now holds the higher hand wins. (All suits have equal value.) What hand should the first man select to assure that he will win?

NOTE: *For those readers who do not play poker, it is sufficient to know that the highest hand is the one containing the Ace, King, Queen, Jack and 10 of the same suit. The next best hand is the King, Queen, Jack, 10, 9 of the same suit, etc.*

45 minutes

73.

In a room 12′ x 12′ x 30′, a spider is on the 12′ x 12′ wall, one foot from the ceiling and midway between the walls. A fly is on the opposite wall, one foot from the floor midway between the walls.

What is the shortest route the spider can take to catch the fly? Of course, the spider is not permitted to fly or drop from ceiling or walls to floor but must move about just by crawling.

2 hours

74.

A sweater worn in the normal way has a label on the inside of the collar. Assuming that the sleeve which accommodates the left arm when the sweater is worn normally is referred to as the left sleeve, where will the label be if the sweater is turned inside out and the right arm is put into the left sleeve and the left arm into the right sleeve?

Will the label be on the front outside, front inside, back outside or back inside? (You are not allowed to use an actual sweater, shirt, etc.)

25 minutes

75.

A suit of 13 cards, Ace, King, Queen, Jack, 10, . . . 2, is arranged in a certain order. The top card is opened, then the card on top is placed at the bottom of the pack and the next card is opened. The next card is placed at the bottom of the pack and again the next card is opened. This procedure is continued until every card is exposed.

If the order of the exposed cards is Ace, King, Queen, Jack, 10, . . . 2, what was the original arrangement of the cards?

(Use of actual cards is not permitted.)

45 minutes

76.

Two men are placing half dollars on a square table, each man placing a coin on the table in turn. The coins are not allowed to overlap and must be completely on the table.

Assuming that each man makes the best possible move available to him, who should be able to place the last coin on the table, the man who placed the first coin or the man who placed the second coin?

45 minutes

77.

A chessboard has 64 squares which can be completely covered by 32 cardboard rectangles, each of which would cover just 2 squares.

Suppose 2 squares of the chessboard at diagonally opposite corners are removed.

Can the modified board be covered with 31 rectangles? If so, how is it done? If not, prove it impossible.

30 minutes

78.

An astronaut is trying to reach a distant heavenly body which, even in these days of fast travel, takes 5 days' traveling time. Furthermore, the vehicle can be fueled with only enough energy to last for 3 days. Assuming that there is an unlimited amount of fuel at the starting point and that fuel can be left for future use at a distance of 1 day's journey, 2 days' journey, 3 days' journey, and 4 days' journey from the starting point, how many days would such a journey take?

HINT: *It can be done in less than 17 days.*

1 hour

79.

Show how to plant 38 trees in such a way that there are 12 rows of trees with 7 trees in each row.

1 hour

80.

A man has 12 coins, one of which is defective in that its weight is not the same as the other 11. In all other respects, the coins are identical.

With the aid of a balance scale how can the man determine which coin is defective and also whether it weighs more or less than the others, provided he is allowed only 3 weighings?

4 hours

super poser group eight score

71 ——		76 ——	
72 ——		77 ——	
73 ——		78 ——	
74 ——		79 ——	
75 ——		80 ——	

total score ——

Super Poser I. Q.
About 50 is startling
65-75 is amazing
Over 75 is fantastic

solutions

1.

Three socks must be taken from the drawer. If only 2 were taken, 1 might be blue and the other brown. The third selection must result in a pair of blue or brown socks.

2.

If the liquid had the qualities claimed for it, the bottle which contained the liquid would have dissolved.

3.

The second car lets the first car get a considerable distance ahead and then travels over the speed limit to catch up.

4.

The man who must move when there are 5 markers left must lose the game because if he removes 1 marker, the other man will take the remaining 4. If he takes 2, the opponent will take the remaining 3, etc. By the same reasoning the man who moves when there are 10 or 15 markers must lose. Therefore, the correct first move is to take away 2 markers and reduce the pile to 15. No matter what your opponent does on his move, you reduce the pile to 10, then to 5, and finally you take the remaining markers.

5.

In order for the train to pass completely through the tunnel, it must travel 2 miles. After 1 mile's travel, the train would be completely in the tunnel, and after another mile it would be completely out. Since the train is traveling at 1 mile a minute, it will take 2 minutes to pass through the tunnel.

6.

If the boys have as many brothers as sisters, then there must be 1 boy more than the number of girls in the family. By trying 2 and 1, 3 and 2, and then 4 and 3, it will be found that 4 boys and 3 girls will fulfill the requirement that each girl has twice as many brothers as sisters.

7.

Only the box in the very center of the stack will elude the paint-brush. All of the other 26 boxes will have at least one side painted.

8.

The carton full of $5 gold pieces is worth more. The denominations of the gold pieces make no difference. The important fact is that the carton containing the $5 gold pieces is full of gold, the other only half full.

9.

The 4th and 11th links must be broken. This will enable the man to pay his rent each day as follows: (Note that by removing the 4th link a chain of 3 links is created; the removal of the 11th link creates a chain of 6 and a chain of 12.)

For the first and second days, the single links are given to the landlord. On the third day he pays with the chain of 3 and takes back the 2 single links. On the fourth and fifth days he gives back a link a day. On the sixth day he takes back the chain of 3 and the single links and gives the chain of 6. By a similar process it can be seen that the man can pay his rent each day through 23 days.

10.

This problem can be solved easily by working backward and determining how much money each man had before each game. Let's suppose that the players are A, B and C, and that A lost the first game, B the second and C the third.

	A	B	C
After third game	$16	$16	$16
Before third game which C lost	8	8	32
Before second game which B lost	4	28	16
Before first game which A lost	26	14	8

The original sums were, therefore, $26, $14, and $8.

11.

The man has 1 half dollar, 1 quarter and 4 dimes.

12.

Three signals can be made—red and white; white and blue; blue and red.

13.

The next layer will contain 9 balls; the next higher layer 4 balls; and the top layer only 1 ball, for a total of 14 additional balls.

14.

The winner will be determined in 49 matches. Every time a match is held, one player is eliminated. To eliminate 49 of the 50 players, 49 matches are required.

15.

In this town, everyone who is asked the question "Are you a Truth Teller or a Liar" must answer, "I am a Truth Teller," because if he actually is he must tell the truth, and if he isn't he must lie and say that he is. A is a Truth Teller and B is a Liar.

16.

When a car travels one mile, each of 4 tires sustains one mile's use. Therefore, when a car has gone 20,000 miles, a total of 80,000 tire miles has been used. Since this mileage was accumulated on 5 tires, each tire must have been used for 16,000 miles.

Another way to look at it is that one "spare" tire replaces each of the other 4 for a period of 4,000 miles so that each tire is used for 16,000 miles and the spare for 4 x 4,000 or 16,000 miles.

17.

If the train schedule brought the uptown train into the station at 1 P.M. and the downtown train at 1:01 P.M.; uptown train at 1:10, downtown at 1:11; uptown at 1:20, downtown at 1:21, etc., each train would be arriving every 10 minutes but his chances of getting the uptown train would be 9 times as great as of getting on the downtown train. For example, if he arrives between 1 P.M.

and 1:01, he goes downtown but if he arrives between 1:01 and
1:10 he goes uptown.

18.
Since the men shared the beer equally, each drank the contents of
2⅔ cans. Therefore, the man who had paid for 5 cans contributed
2⅓ and the man who bought 3 cans contributed ⅓ of a can to make
up the third man's share. Since the first man's contribution was 7
times that of the second, the correct division is 70¢ to the first man
and 10¢ to the second.
Here is another way to look at it. If 80¢ is the cost of 2⅔ cans,
each can must cost 30¢. The first man spent $1.50 and the second
90¢ for a total of $2.40. In order for the cost to be the same for
each man, the first man's expense must be reduced by 70¢ and
the second by 10¢ for the cost to be 80¢ to each of the three men.

19.

20.
The difficulty in this problem is in getting the mental set which sug-
gests that the lines can extend beyond the outside borders of the
original 9 dots.

21.
If we designate the 3 men A, B and C and their respective wives
a, b and c, the crossings can be shown in diagram form as follows:

69

```
                    A B C a b c
Step  1    A B C a    ⟶            b c
Step  2    A B C a b  ⟵              c
Step  3    A B C      ⟶          a b c
Step  4    A B C a    ⟵            b c
Step  5    A      a   ⟶    B C    b c
Step  6    A B    a b ⟵      C      c
Step  7           a b ⟶ A B C      c
Step  8           a b c ⟵ A B C
Step  9           a   ⟶ A B C    b c
Step 10           a b ⟵ A B C      c
Step 11               ⟶ A B C a b c
```

22.

If the matches are designated 1 through 6 from left to right, the desired position can be obtained by turning over matches 2 and 3; 3 and 4; and then 4 and 5.

23.

The procedure for obtaining 4 quarts can most easily be shown in diagram form as follows:

	8 Qt. Jug	5 Qt. Jug	3 Qt. Jug
	8	0	0
Step 1	3	5	0
Step 2	3	2	3
Step 3	6	2	0
Step 4	6	0	2
Step 5	1	5	2
Step 6	1	4	3
Step 7	4	4	0

24.

The obvious answer, 6, is incorrect because after the 6 cigarettes have been smoked there will again be 6 butts which can be made into another cigarette. The answer is, therefore, 7.

25.

Take three markers from the pile of 5 leaving piles of 3, 2 and 1. Any move by your opponent is countered by leaving piles of 2 and 2 or piles of 1 and 1, which are obviously losing positions for your opponent. Any move other than changing the 5 to a 2 is losing for you because your opponent could then get you into the 3, 2, 1 position, which we know is losing, or into the 3, 3, or 1, 1 positions, which are also obviously losing.

26.

Simply by reversing the 20 cards she holds. The reasoning is as follows: Let's suppose that in the remainder of the deck there were 15 cards reversed. Then the lady would have been holding 20 cards of which 5 were reversed. By turning the deck of 20 cards over, she now has 5 cards face down and 15 (matching those in the remainder of the deck) turned over. The fact is that the lady never knows how many cards were turned over in each of the two parts of the deck but, by turning over her 20 cards, she can always match the number turned over in the remainder of the deck.

27.

Assuming only 4 coins remained in the morning, this would mean that the third man must have found 7 coins left when he arrived. But 7 is not $\frac{2}{3}$ of a whole number, so this is impossible. The next possibility is 7 coins left in the morning, which we have already discovered is impossible. The next possibility is 10, which is $\frac{2}{3}$ of 15. This means the third man found 16 coins, took one and then took 5 more. The second man then must have found 25 coins, taken one and then taken 8 more. However, 25 is not $\frac{2}{3}$ of a whole number and, therefore, the assumption that 10 coins remained in the morning is incorrect. By similar reasoning 13, 16 and 19 can be eliminated but 22 is found to meet the required conditions. The third man found 34, took one and left $\frac{2}{3}$ of 33 or 22; the second man found 52, took one and left $\frac{2}{3}$ of 51 or 34; the first man found 79, took one and left $\frac{2}{3}$ of 78 or 52. The answer is 79 coins were hidden.

28.

If we had a number between 2,000 and 3,000 which was exactly divisible by 2, 3, 4, 5, 6, 7, 8 and 9, then by adding one we would have the required number. If 9 is multiplied by 8, that product will be divisible by 9 and 8 and, of course, by 2, 3 and 6 as well. Now if 9 x 8 is further multiplied by 5 and 7, the result 9 x 8 x 7 x 5 or 2,520 will be divisible by all the numbers from 2 through 9. The number of men in the battalion was 2,521.

29.

The king took one object from the first workman; two from the second; three from the third, etc. In total, he took $1 + 2 + 3 + 4 + 5 + 6 + 7 + 8 + 9 + 10 + 11 + 12 + 13 + 14 + 15 + 16 + 17 + 18 + 19 + 20$ or 210 objects. If all were of full weight, the objects would weigh 210 ounces. If the first artisan was cheating, the total would be short by $\frac{1}{8}$ ounce; if the second, the shortage would be $\frac{1}{4}$ ounce; if the fifth man, the shortage would be $\frac{5}{8}$ ounce, etc.

30.

From statement 6, Arthur is established as the painter. From statements 2, 3 and 4, Arthur cannot be teacher, writer, engineer or doctor and is therefore the lawyer. Arthur is then a painter and a lawyer. Now Ben is not a writer from statement 5, so his occupations must be chosen from doctor, teacher and engineer. From statement 1, the doctor and teacher are two different people so Ben must be an engineer. He cannot also be a doctor because that would leave teacher and writer for Charles, which statement 2 forbids. Ben must be a teacher and Charles is a doctor and a writer.

31.

One mug can be placed on top of the other and the saucer placed on top of the upper mug. One mug is thus serving in place of the missing saucer.

32.

If the coat cost $100 and the hat $10, the difference would be $90.

Therefore, the coat must cost more and the hat less. A little reflection indicates the coat costs $105 and the hat costs $5 so the difference in cost is $100.

33.

34.
The bookworm chewed through two covers only or ½ inch. When a book is on a bookshelf, the first page of the book is next to the cover on the right-hand side and the last page is next to the cover on the left-hand side as one faces the bookshelf. Consequently, the bookworm started by eating through the cover of the first volume and then through the cover of the second volume.

35.
The container would be half full on the 59th day. Since the number of bacteria doubles each day, the container must have been half full on the day before it became full.

36.
The transfer of the sexes can be accomplished as follows: In the diagram below, M stands for a man, W for a woman. Ⓜ and Ⓦ identify the man and woman who know how to row.

	M M M M Ⓜ	W W W W Ⓦ
Step 1	M M M	W W W W Ⓦ M Ⓜ
Step 2	M M M W W Ⓦ	W W M Ⓜ
Step 3	M M W W	W W Ⓦ M M Ⓜ
Step 4	M M Ⓜ W W Ⓦ	W W M M
Step 5	M Ⓜ W W	W W Ⓦ M M M
Step 6	M Ⓜ W W W W Ⓦ	M M M
Step 7	W W W W Ⓦ	M M M M Ⓜ

37.

In striking 7, the clock strikes its first tone at 7 o'clock, then strikes 6 more times at regular intervals. These 6 intervals take 7 seconds so that the intervals between tones is $1\frac{1}{6}$ seconds. To strike 10, there are 9 intervals each taking $1\frac{1}{6}$ seconds for a total of $10\frac{1}{2}$ seconds.

38.

The amount of water in the original alcohol container exactly equals the amount of alcohol in the original water container. This becomes clear when you consider that, after the mixing is completed, each container still holds a gallon of liquid. Any alcohol which was transferred from the alcohol container to the water container must have been replaced with an identical amount of water.

39.

The solution to this problem can best be explained by a concrete example. Assume the clock in the man's home was started when the clock showed 12 o'clock. On arrival at the friend's house the correct time was 2 P.M. and on leaving the time was 4 P.M. When the man got home, the time was 2:30 P.M. on his clock. This means that the complete trip took $2\frac{1}{2}$ hours and the walking time must have been 30 minutes, or 15 minutes each way. Since he left his friend's house at 4 P.M., the correct time when he got home was 4:15 P.M.

40.

When the trains are moving in opposite directions, they are passing each other with the combined speeds of the two trains; when going in the same direction, the "passing speed" is the speed of the passenger train minus the speed of the freight train. If the passenger train goes twice as fast as the freight train, then the passing speed when going in opposite directions will be 2 plus 1 or 3 compared with 2 minus 1 or 1 when the trains are going in the same direction. The answer is twice as fast.

41.

Since there were 60 eyes, there must have been 30 animals. The question then is what combination of 4-legged rabbits and 2-legged chickens totaling 30 will give 86 feet. A little experimentation will give the answer—13 rabbits and 17 chickens.

42.

The storekeeper's loss must equal the customer's gain which was $4 plus the shoes, or, since the shoes cost the storekeeper $3, his total loss was $7.

43.

The first 3 choices might yield 1 of each color, but on the 4th choice there must be at least 2 of one color. The answer is, therefore, 4.

44.

The painted area is shown in the diagram below. The clear area is not 4' x 4' but it does measure 4' from top to bottom and from side to side.

45.

Since the original group totaled approximately 1,000 men and they marched in a square formation, there must have been either 900, 961, 1,024 or 1,089 men. Now it is just a matter of testing to determine which of these numbers meets the stated conditions.

900 − 10 = 890 which is not divisible by 6.

961 − 10 = 951 which is not divisible by 6.

1,024 − 10 = 1,014 which gives 169 (or 13 x 13) when divided by 6. Also 1,014 − 6 = 1,008 which when divided by 7 gives 144 (a 12 x 12 square formation). There were, therefore, 1,024 men in the group.

46.

The middle man said, "I sometimes tell the truth and sometimes I lie." If this statement were true, then the other 2 men would both be lying, which would mark the middle man as a truth teller. But then his statement would be false. So, the middle man must be the man who always lies. Therefore, the man at the left must be the one who always tells the truth and the third man, at the right, is the man who sometimes tells the truth and sometimes lies.

47.

Fifteen moves are required. If we call the discs 1, 2, 3, 4, the smallest being 1, etc., the procedure is shown in chart form as follows:

	1 2 3 4		
Step 1	2 3 4	1	
Step 2	3 4	1	2
Step 3	3 4		1 2
Step 4	4	3	1 2
Step 5	1 4	3	2
Step 6	1 4	2 3	
Step 7	4	1 2 3	
Step 8		1 2 3	4
Step 9		2 3	1 4
Step 10	2	3	1 4
Step 11	1 2	3	4
Step 12	1 2		3 4
Step 13	2	1	3 4
Step 14		1	2 3 4
Step 15			1 2 3 4

48.

Three coins are weighed against 3 other coins. If the scale balances, the defective coin is among the 3 not weighed. Two of these coins are then weighed against each other, and if they don't balance the lighter one is the defective coin. If they balance, the coin not weighed is the defective one.

If on the first weighing the scale doesn't balance, the 3 among which the lighter coin may be found will be identified and the defective coin can be found as shown above from among the 3 in one additional weighing.

49.
Since they arrived home 10 minutes earlier than usual, the point at which they met must have been 5 minutes' riding time from the station. The wife should have been at that point at five minutes to six. Since the husband started to walk at 5 o'clock, he must have been walking for 55 minutes when he met his wife.

50.
Let us call the men A, B and C and follow the reasoning of A. When his blindfold was removed, he saw spots on B and C and reasoned that B might be raising his hand because of C's spot and C might be raising his hand because of B's spot, which would explain why all 3 men raised their hands and no one knew whether he himself had a spot. However, A continued to reason as follows: Suppose I do not have a spot. Then B looking at me and C would know that C is raising his hand because of B's spot and he would immediately announce that he had a spot. Since he didn't announce his spot immediately, it could only be because I have a spot.

51.
The first boat going east moves into the inlet. The 3 boats going west pass the inlet and the east-bound boat in the inlet is free to continue its journey. The west-bound boats return to their original positions and another east-bound boat goes into the inlet. Again the west-bound boats pass the inlet and the second east-bound boat moves out of the inlet and away. This procedure is repeated for the last east-bound boat.

52.
The man made $20. He made $10 when he sold the item for the first time and another $10 when he sold it for the second time.

53.

The stranger suggested that each should get on the other's horse. Note that the poser states "the man whose horse crosses the finish line, etc."

54.

Since the trains travel at 25 miles per hour, they will meet after traveling for 1 hour. The bird also must have been flying for 1 hour and since it traveled at 100 miles per hour, the bird flew 100 miles.

55.

There are 28 dominoes as follows:

```
0 can be combined with 0, 1, 2, 3, 4, 5, 6 giving 7 dominoes.
1 can be combined with    1, 2, 3, 4, 5, 6 giving 6 dominoes.
2 can be combined with       2, 3, 4, 5, 6 giving 5 dominoes.
3 can be combined with          3, 4, 5, 6 giving 4 dominoes.
4 can be combined with             4, 5, 6 giving 3 dominoes.
5 can be combined with                5, 6 giving 2 dominoes.
6 can be combined with                   6 giving 1 domino.
```

Totaling 7 + 6 + 5 + 4 + 3 + 2 + 1 gives a total of 28.

56.

If you assume Abe is the criminal, Charlie's and Dan's statements are true.
If you assume Bert is the criminal, Abe's and Dan's statements are true.
If you assume Dan is the criminal, Bert's and Charlie's statements are true.
Therefore, Charlie is the criminal and only Dan's statement is true.

57.

The procedure in chart form is as follows:

		19 Qt.	13 Qt.	7 Qt.
		0	13	7
Step	1	7	13	0
Step	2	19	1	0
Step	3	12	1	7
Step	4	12	8	0
Step	5	5	8	7
Step	6	5	13	2
Step	7	18	0	2
Step	8	18	2	0
Step	9	11	2	7
Step	10	11	9	0
Step	11	4	9	7
Step	12	4	13	3
Step	13	17	0	3
Step	14	17	3	0
Step	15	10	3	7

58.

59.

If the checkers are designated 1 through 10 from left to right:

Step 1 Checker No. 4 covers No. 1.
Step 2 Checker No. 6 covers No. 9.
Step 3 Checker No. 8 covers No. 3.
Step 4 Checker No. 2 covers No. 5.
Step 5 Checker No. 10 covers No. 7.

60.

The ship out of New York will meet the Liverpool ship which left 6 days ago at the dock in New York. Thereafter, it will meet a ship every half day, including a ship just leaving Liverpool when the

New York ship arrives. In total, 13 ships from Liverpool will be met. Another way of looking at it is that on the day the New York ship leaves, let's say the 15th of the month, the ship that left Liverpool on the 9th will be arriving. The New York ship will then meet all Liverpool ships which left between the 9th and the 21st, which is 13 ships.

61.

If a brick balances ¾ of a brick and ¾ of a pound, then ¼ of a brick must weigh ¾ of a pound and a whole brick will weigh 3 pounds.

62.

63.

The frog gets to the top on the 6th day. He advances 1' per day for the first 5 days. On that day he gets up as high as 9' but falls back to 5', then on the 6th day he gets to the top.

64.

The answer is 16. Note that if you were allowed 1 cut, you would get 2 pieces. Two cuts will give you 4 pieces; three cuts gives 7 pieces; four cuts, 11 pieces; and five cuts, 16 pieces. In chart form this increase in the number of pieces can be seen to be equal to the "cut" number. Thus, if a sixth cut were made, the pie would be divided into 22 pieces.

Number of Cuts	Number of Pieces	Number of Pieces Added
1	2	–
2	4	2
3	7	3
4	11	4
5	16	5

65.

Only the numbers 0, 1, 6, 8 and 9 can be turned upside down and still be read as a number. The numbers 0, 1 and 8 remain 0, 1 and 8 when turned over; 6 becomes 9 and 9 becomes 6. The possible numbers on the bus were, therefore, 9, 16, 81, 100, 169 or 196. The number on the bus must have been 196 because 961 is a perfect square (31 x 31).

66.

Only one sampling from the box marked "Black, White" is necessary. If the marble is white, that means the other marble in that box is also white; otherwise, the label would have been correct. Now the box marked "Black, Black" cannot have two black marbles nor can it have two white marbles because we already know the box marked "Black, White" has two white ones. The "Black, Black" box must have a black and white marble and the remaining box marked "White, White" must have two black marbles.

67.

The weights must be 1 lb., 3 lbs. and 9 lbs. Two is obtained by putting the 3 lb. weight on one side and the 1 lb. weight on the other side. The other weights are obtained as follows:

$$4 = 1 + 3$$
$$5 = 9 \text{ on one side and } 3 + 1 \text{ on the other}$$
$$6 = 9 \text{ on one side and } 3 \text{ on the other}$$
$$7 = 9 + 1 \text{ on one side and } 3 \text{ on the other}$$
$$8 = 9 \text{ on one side and } 1 \text{ on the other}$$
$$10 = 9 + 1$$
$$11 = 9 + 3 \text{ on one side and } 1 \text{ on the other}$$
$$12 = 9 + 3$$
$$13 = 9 + 3 + 1$$

68.

Since 10 applicants had had neither mathematics nor biology training, we can concern ourselves with the other 90 applicants only. Of these, 20 had had no mathematics and 8 had had no biology training. The remainder, 62, must, therefore, have had both mathematics and biology.

69.

The only numbers that can be read upside down are 0, 1, 6, 8 and 9. The problem then is to arrange these 5 numbers so that when turned upside down the result will be 78,633 larger. A little experimentation will show the number to be 10,968 which becomes 89,601 when inverted.

70.

The cheapest method is to open the 4 links of one section and then use these links to join the other 4 sections together. The total cost would be 80 cents. The more obvious method of opening links of each section would cost $1.

71.

Six cuts are required; it cannot be done in less. This is apparent when you consider the cube which is formed in the middle of the original cube—the one which has no exposed surface. Since a cube has 6 sides, the saw must create this cube by 6 individual cuts, and no matter how the slices are rearranged this cube requires 6 passes of the saw.

72.

The winning selection is 10S, 10H, 10C and 10D with any other card. If the second man does not take a card higher than a 10 in each suit, the first man can obviously select a Royal Flush (Ace, King, Queen, Jack, 10 of the same suit). If the second man does select cards higher than 10 in each suit, the first man chooses a straight flush up to the 10 on his second selection and the highest hand the second man can get is a straight flush up to a 9 since all 10's were already taken by the first man. (Other winning hands are 3 10's and any of the following two cards from the other suits: A, 9; K, 9; Q, 9; J, 9; K, 8; Q, 8; J, 8; Q, 7; J, 7; J, 6.)

73.

Although it would seem that walking straight down to the floor then across the floor and up one foot on the opposite wall would be the shortest route, it is not. This route would, of course, be 42′ (11′ down, 30′ across and 1′ up). The shortest route actually is a fairly complicated one in which the spider walks on 5 of the 6 surfaces, ceiling, floor and 3 walls as indicated in the diagram below. This route is only 40′ and can be seen more easily by "cracking" the room open. (Use of a paper model might help.)

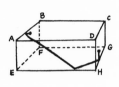 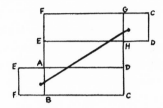

74.

The label will be on the back outside. Now you can turn a sweater inside out and prove it.

75.

Shown below are the 13 cards:

1	2	3	4	5	6	7	8	9	10	11	12	13
A		K		Q		J		10		9		8
			7				6			5		
	3				4				2			

Obviously, the 1st card must be the Ace, the 3rd card the King, 5th card the Queen, etc., as shown in the diagram. Now the 2nd card is at the top of the deck followed by 4th, 6th, 8th, 10th and 12th cards. The 2nd card must be put at the bottom and, therefore, the 4th card is the next exposed and must be the 7; next card goes to the bottom so the 8th card is next exposed and is the 6. The 10th card is buried and the 12th card becomes the 5. Now only the 2nd, 6th and 10th cards are left. By similar reasoning the 6th card is the 4, the 2nd card is the 3 and the 10th card is the 2. The complete correct order of the cards is A, 3, K, 7, Q, 4, J, 6, 10, 2, 9, 5, 8.

76.

The man who places the first coin should win. He should place the first coin so that the middle of the coin covers the exact middle of the table. Then when the second player places a coin the first player places his in a position symmetrical with respect to the center. For example, if the second player puts a coin in the extreme upper left-hand corner of the table, the first player puts a coin in the extreme lower right-hand corner. If the first player continues to "duplicate" moves, eventually there will be no space left for the second player to place another coin.

77.

It is impossible to cover the board with 31 rectangles. Each rectangle covers 1 white square and 1 black square because, on a chessboard, a white and black square are always adjacent. Now the 2 squares which were removed are of the same color so the remaining board has 2 more boxes of one color than the other. After the rectangles have covered 60 boxes, there will be left 2 squares of the same color and obviously the remaining rectangle cannot cover these two squares.

78.

The journey would take 15 days. The most economical method is to get 1 day's fuel at the point which is 1 day's flight from the starting point and 1 day's fuel at the 2-day station. Then with a full supply of 3 days' fuel, the journey can be made in 5 days. To get one day's fuel at the 1-day station and get back to the starting point requires 2 days' journey. To get 1 day's fuel at the 2-day station requires 8 days—4 days to get 2 days' fuel at 1-day station and 4 days to go from starting point to 2-day station and back. Consequently, the whole trip takes 2 days plus 8 days plus 5 days or 15 days.

79.

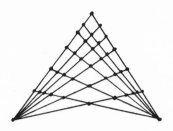

80.
1. Take 4 coins and weigh them against 4 other coins. If the scale balances, the defective coin is among the remaining 4 coins.
2. Of the remaining 4 coins, weigh 3 against 3 normal coins. If the scale balances, the defective coin is the 4th of the suspected coins and one additional weighing will determine if it is heavier or lighter than the other coins.
3. If the 3 coins discussed in 2 above do not balance against the 3 normal coins, this weighing will have determined whether the defective coin is heavier or lighter then the rest. If the suspected coin is lighter than the rest, 2 of the 3 can be weighed against each other and the side of the scale which is "up" contains the defective coin. If the scale balances, the 3rd of the suspected coins is the defective one and it is lighter than the others. (The same considerations apply, of course, if the 3 suspected coins prove heavier than the normal ones.)
Now we come to the more difficult part. In step 1, we assumed that the first weighing of 4 coins against 4 coins resulted in a balanced scale. Now we will examine the other possibility—suppose the scale does not balance.
4. If the scale does not balance, this establishes 4 coins (those not on the scale) as being normal and also earmarks 4 coins as having among them the potentially heavier coin and 4 coins among which the defectively light one would be found.

85

5. (Here is the crucial step.) For purposes of clarity, we will use the letter H to designate each of the 4 coins suspected of being heavy and L to designate each of the 4 coins suspected of being light. N will designate the coins which are known to be normal. The next weighing will then be 3 H's and 1 L against 1 H and 3 N's, leaving 3 L's and 1 N off the scale.

6. If the scale balances, one of the 3 L's left off the scale is defective and the same procedure as indicated in step 3 above will determine the defectively light coin.

7. If the scale does not balance, there are two possibilities. Either the side with the 3 H's and 1 L is heavier than the other side or it is lighter.

(a) If it is heavier, this means that one of the 3 H's on that side of the scale is defective and heavier than the rest and again the procedure of step 3 will determine the exact defective coin.

(b) If it is lighter, this means that either the L on that side of the scale is defectively lighter or the H on the other side of the scale is heavier. The defective coin can be determined by weighing either suspect against a normal coin.